Winning

Iris Howden

Published in association with
The Basic Skills Agency

Acknowledgements
Cover: Stephanie Hawken
Illustrations: Maureen Carter

Orders; please contact Bookpoint Ltd, 39 Milton Park, Abingdon, Oxon OX14
4TD. Telephone: (44) 01235 400414, Fax: (44) 01235 400454. Lines are open
from 9.00–6.00, Monday to Saturday, with a 24 hour message answering service.
Email address: orders@bookpoint.co.uk

British Library Cataloguing in Publication Data
A catalogue record for this title is available from the British Library

ISBN 0 340 77608 0

First published 2000
Impression number   10 9 8 7 6 5 4 3 2 1
Year   2005 2004 2003 2002 2001 2000

Typeset by GreenGate Publishing Services, Tonbridge, Kent.
Printed in Great Britain for Hodder and Stoughton Educational, a division of
Hodder Headline Plc, 338 Euston Road, London NW1 3BH, by Atheneum
Press, Gateshead, Tyne & Wear

Winning

Contents

1

Liz

I've always loved horses.
They've been a part of my life
ever since I was a little girl.
My grandfather used to be a jockey.
When I was small he would take me
to the local stables.
He'd hold me up to pat the horses.
I loved to stroke their noses.
They felt as soft as velvet.

When I was seven I got my first pony.
Grandad taught me to ride.
I took to it right away.
Grandad said I was a natural.
Soon I was able to trot and canter.
I could make my pony do what I wanted.
Then I learned to jump.
I'd put him over our home-made jumps.

As the years went on I won prizes.
My bedroom walls were hung with
the rosettes I'd won at horse shows.
A shelf was filled with silver cups.

When I left school I knew I wanted
to work with horses.
I told my mum I wanted to work
in a racing stable.
She nearly had a fit.
'That's no job for a girl,' she said.
'Riding race horses.
Do you know how many jockeys
are injured every year?

Some of them get killed.
Your grandfather was lucky.
He never had a serious accident
but he still broke lots of bones.'

But Grandad took my side.
'Let the lass make up her own mind,'
he told Mum.
I could have kissed him.
He wrote off to one of his old friends –
a man called Tim O'Brien.
Grandad and Tim had been jockeys together
when they were young.

Tim was now head lad at a racing stable
near York.
The next week I got a letter back.
It asked me to go for an interview.
They were taking on some school leavers.
I was very happy. I couldn't wait to go.

My mum drove me to the stables.
She dropped me off at the gate.

I could tell it was a well run place.
It was all so neat and clean.
Tim O'Brien was a small man
with an Irish accent.
He walked with a limp.
Grandad told me that a bad fall
had left him lame.

He was very down to earth.
'Right missie,' he said straight away.
'Let's see what you can do.'
He led a big bay horse out of its box.
He handed me a helmet.
I was quite nervous.
It seemed a long way from the ground.
This was quite different from riding
my old pony round a field.
This was an animal built for speed.
It was full of spirit and very strong.
I knew I had to take control.

'Walk on,' Tim shouted. 'Go into the field.'
I felt the horse respond to my hands
and heels.
I began to enjoy myself.
I had never ridden a horse with such power.
I made it walk, trot and canter
at Tim's command.
I rode in a circle as he watched.

At last he called me over.
He told me to dismount.
'You'll do,' he said. 'Start on Monday.
I'll fix it with Mr Mason, the owner.
Don't expect any favours mind.
Just because you're Len's granddaughter.'
I had got the job.

2

The Stables

I was not the only girl at the stables.
Jill had worked there for a year.
She was a big help to me.
She showed me the ropes.
I was to share her digs in the village.
We biked into work each day.

We were hard at work by seven.
At first I got all the dirty jobs. I had to
muck out the stalls and sweep the yard.
I also had to wash the horses' smelly rugs.

The stable lads made fun of me.
They called me Skinny Lizzie.
'Take no notice,' Jill said.
'It's just because you're new.'

There were four lads.
Sam and Joe were brothers.
They were real jokers.
'Daft as brushes,' Tim called them.
Another lad, Neil, was deaf.
He was very quiet and kept himself to himself.
He could lip read and as I had learned
to sign a bit at school, we got on okay.

The last one, Paul Jackson,
was known as Jacko.
He was horrible. A real big head.
He thought he was a cut above us
because he got more rides.
He was always smarming around Tim.
Not that we called him Tim to his face.
He was always 'Boss' or 'Mr O'Brien.'

Tim was hard on all of us.
A word of praise was very rare.
He took me by surprise one day by saying,
'You're doing well, Liz.
You can ride out today.'
So far he'd only let me walk the horses out
or bring them back from exercise.

Weeks passed and I learned a lot.
How to groom a horse and care for its tack.
The right amount to feed it and
how to check for any signs of illness.
We each had several horses to look after.
I felt part of the team now.
The lads stopped trying to wind me up.
Sometimes Jill and I met them after work.
We'd have a game of pool at the village pub.

I never saw much of Mr Mason, the owner.
He was the trainer but he was often
busy in the office.

Sometimes Mr Mason went over to Ireland.
He brought back young horses to train.
He hoped to find one that would
win a big money prize.

One day a new horse arrived.
I was put in charge of it.
'It's a nervy thing,' Tim told me.
'It needs a gentle touch.'
He ran his hands along the horse's back
and down its legs.
'It's a good strong beast,' he said.
'It could do well.'

The horse's name was Whitby Jet.
We called it Jet for short.
He was very dark brown, almost black
with large shiny eyes.
He had a white star on his forehead.
I fell for Jet right away.
I'd spend ages grooming him.
Brushing his mane and tail.
Oiling his hooves.

Tim saw how I felt about Jet.
'Don't go getting too fond
of that animal,' he said.
'If he doesn't win any races he'll be sold.'
I knew he was warning me for my own good
but I couldn't help loving Jet.
He was really special.
I knew he'd be a winner.

3

Jet

Jet wasn't an easy ride.
Some days he'd be up at the front.
Pushing ahead, keen to lead.
At other times the slightest thing
would spook him, like a branch
flapping in the hedge.
'We'll have to school him,' Tim told me.

One of the things Jet hated most
was going in the starting gate.
This was a real problem.

A horse that's fussy about that
can get off to a bad start in a race.
I spent ages coaching him.
I'd lead him into the gate we'd set up
and talk to him, making him feel safe.

Neil helped me.
He'd ride Jet while I led him through.
Neil had a nice way with horses.
He was quiet and calm.

Jacko was quite different.
I had to admit he was a good rider.
He would make it as a jockey.
He was the sort who went all out to win
but he always had to show off.
He let the horse know who was boss
and he had a cruel streak.

One day he came up to us.
'Why if it isn't Jenny Pitman –
the famous woman trainer,' he sneered,
'and her leading jockey Lester Piggot.'

This was a dig at Neil's deafness.
I tried to ignore him.
'Tim says I've to give Jet a gallop,' he said.
My heart sank.
I knew Jet had to get used to other riders
but I didn't want Jacko to be one of them.

I went back to the yard.
It was time to clean the tack.
It wasn't a job I liked. I washed and dried
the bits and the stirrup irons.
I rubbed saddle soap into the bridle straps.
But my mind wasn't on the job.
I was wondering how Jet was doing
with Jacko on board.

I soon found out.
Suddenly there was a lot of noise outside.
I could hear Tim's voice.
He was shouting at someone.
Tim didn't very often lose his temper.
When he did we all took cover.
I peeped out through the stable door.

Jet was standing in the yard.
He was in a sweat and trembling.
I'd never seen him in such a state.
Jacko stood nearby. He hung his head
while Tim raged at him.
'If I ever see you treat a horse
like that again,' Tim shouted,
'you'll get your cards straight away.'

He snatched the whip from Jacko's hand.
I thought he was going to hit Jacko
with it but he flung it to the ground.
'Liz, come out here,' he shouted.
'Take Jet in and sponge him down.'

I ran out to the yard and took Jet's reins.
'You've undone weeks of good work
by this lass,' Tim went on.
Jacko was getting a real roasting.
I risked a glance at him.
His face was white with anger.
Jacko scowled at me as he left.
I knew I had made an enemy.

It was then that I saw there
was someone else in the yard.
A tall young man in his early twenties
stood watching us.
He was good looking with fair hair,
and a suntan.
He was wearing chinos and a denim jacket.

Tim began to calm down.
He called him over to meet me.
'Mr Bailey, this is Liz.
Liz, meet Mr Mike Bailey.
He's our new assistant trainer.
I'm very sorry you had to witness that,
Mr Bailey,' Tim said.
The young man held out his hand.
'Good to meet you, Liz,' he said.
'Please, both of you, call me Mike.'
He looked really nice.
I had the feeling we would get on.

4

Jet's First Race

Mike and I soon became friends.
Mike was our boss but he wasn't stuffy.
He was soon one of us.
He'd join us for a game of pool.
'I like Mike,' Jill told me one night.
'But I think he fancies you.'
'Don't be daft,' I said.
'We work together, that's all.'

Mike had asked me to help him
break in one of the young horses.
I was really pleased.
Schooling horses was what I liked best.
'You've got the knack,' Mike said.
'You're so gentle with them.'

The horse was a grey filly called New Dawn.
We spent a lot of time leading her
round the field on a lunge rein.
Then we had to get her used to a bridle and
the feel of the bit in her mouth.
Next we put a saddle on her back.

At last Mike thought it was time to try
her with a rider on board.
He asked Neil to help out.
'You two work well together,' Mike said.
'Is he your boyfriend?'
'No,' I said. 'We're just friends.
I wish Mr Mason would take Neil on as
an apprentice. He's really keen to be a jockey.'
'I'll speak to him about it,' Mike said.

Neil was over the moon.
He was too shy to ask for himself.
I was pleased I had put Mike in the picture
about us. I liked Mike a lot.
I wanted him to ask me out.
It wasn't long before he did.
He took me for a meal in a pub
called the Red Dragon.
A lot of the racing crowd went there.

The first person we saw was Jacko.
He was with a bunch of lads from Baxters –
a rival stables near by.
Jacko gave me a dirty look as we came in.
'Keeping in with the boss?' he said
as I passed him.

There were some jockeys in the bar.
One of them, Alan Evans, often rode for us.
He came over to our table.
'I hear I'm to ride Whitby Jet for you,' he said.
'I'll be down soon to try him out.'

After his ride Alan was all smiles.
He patted Jet on the neck.
'He seems like a good bet,' Alan said.
'He's very willing.
He should do okay on Saturday.'

On Friday night I could hardly sleep.
I was so excited.
I could picture myself leading Jet
into the winner's enclosure.
'Don't build your hopes up,'
Mike warned me. 'Jet's a young horse.
He's got a lot to learn.'

The next day I went with Jet in the horse box.
I had groomed him so well
his coat shone like silk.
I kissed him on the nose.
'Good luck,' I said. 'I know you can do it.'
I hoped he would not react badly
to the crowds and the noise.
That he would get off to a good start.

It was all over so fast.
The horses flashed past the stand twice.
Each time the jockeys were a blur of colours.
It was hard to see where Jet was.
Then I saw him coming up to the last fence.
I shouted at the top of my voice.
'Come on Jet, come on.'
I hoped he would take the lead.

It was between Jet and a big chestnut
called Ready or Not.
At that moment a loose horse ran
between them.
Alan had to swerve to avoid it.
The chestnut romped home first.
I heard the tannoy announce it as the winner.

'Cheer up,' Mike said later.
'Coming second was brilliant
for his first time out.
Alan said Jet ran really well.
He had plenty of speed left at the end.
Well done, Jet, and well done you,' he said,
giving me a kiss.

I felt so happy driving back.
Things couldn't be better.
Jet had proved he could win.
Mike and I were getting close.
Everything was going my way.

5

Foul Play

On Jet's next time out it all went wrong.
I had a puncture on my way to work.
By the time I got to the stables
the horse box was being loaded.
Tim was in a foul mood.
'Come on, Liz, get in,' he snapped.
'We can't wait all day.
It's a long drive to Hexham.'
We were off to a bad start.

When we reached the ground
Mike went to the weighing room to find Alan.
Then he had to enter Jet's name
at the Clerk of the Course's office.
We were running short of time.

Jet was in the two o'clock race.
Shortly before the off I heard
my name called over the tannoy.
'Would Miss Liz Dale come to the
Steward's Office.' It took me by surprise.
Who would want to speak to me?
I threw my rucksack down and set off.
When I got there the caller had rung off.
I was puzzled. What could it mean?

I rushed back to the stand.
I had missed the start of the race.
'How's he doing?' I gasped,
out of breath from running.
'Not too badly,' Mike said.

'But he'll have his work cut out.
There are some good horses running.
Hexham's a hilly course.
It takes a lot out of them.'

There were two strong front runners,
Fly By Night and Belmont Tiger.
Fly By Night was the favourite.
At the end of the first circuit
Jet was way behind them.
'He'll never make it now,' Mike said.
He sounded really down.
I couldn't believe it. Jet had a big heart.
He would always keep going.

I watched in horror as Jet fell back.
Soon he was in a bunch of horses
right at the back.
Then I saw him wobble from side to side.
He came to a halt with his head down.
I wanted to duck under the rails and run
across the course to find out what was wrong.
Mike held me back.

The rest of that day was a nightmare.
Alan and Mike had to see the Steward.
Tests were to be carried out on Jet.
I waited for what seemed like hours.
When they came back, I could tell
from their faces something was wrong.
They told me Jet had been drugged.
Someone had given him dope to slow
him down.

The police were called.
They went over every inch of our horse box.
Mike and I were both searched.
Then a policeman picked up my rucksack.

He looked in all the pockets.
He held something out to show us.
It was a plastic bag.
Inside he found a small bottle.
There was a syringe with it.
A needle was still in it.
'Can you explain how these things
came to be in your rucksack?' he asked me.

That night I was sent home in disgrace.
Mr Mason told me I was to stay there
until an enquiry had been carried out.
I was not to come back to work.
I had been suspended.

6

Things Get Worse

The days at home dragged by.
I couldn't eat or sleep. I was so worried.
My grandad tried to cheer me up.
'I'll phone Tim O'Brien,' he said.
'Anyone can see you love horses.
You'd never harm one.'
'No, Grandad,' I said. 'It won't do any good.'

I could still picture the scene in the yard.

When we got back, Mr Mason
had called all the staff together.
'This girl has let the stable down,'
he told them.
'You know the rules. Anyone caught
trying to fix a race gets the sack.
But I'm a fair man.
I'll wait for the result of the police enquiry.'
No-one had dared to speak.

Since then I had had one phone call from Jill.
'Keep your chin up,' she said.
'We're all behind you.'
There was a note from Neil which said,
'I'll look after Jet till you get back.'
He'd put a photo of Jet in with it.
It was a nice thought but I could
hardly bear to look at it.

Mike sent a postcard with
'DON'T GIVE UP HOPE'
written on the back. That was all.
'Don't give up hope!' I thought.
It was easy for him to say.
I missed him a lot. He didn't seem
to feel the same about me.

Things went from bad to worse.
The police came to interview me again.
Then I heard I was being charged.
I would have to go to court.
My mum got me a solicitor.

'I didn't do it,' I told him.
'And that's the truth.'
'But it looks bad,' he said.
'You were on the spot, Liz.
The drugs were found in your bag.'
I cried myself to sleep that night.

Next day the local papers sent reporters
round to see me.
Grandad wouldn't answer the door.
'Go away,' he shouted at them.
'No comment. We've got nothing to say.'
'If this gets in the papers,' I said,
'I'll never get another job with horses.
No trainer will ever trust me.'
My career with horses was over
before it had begun.

7

Good News

The trial was in a month's time.
I was already a nervous wreck.
How could I wait so long?

One afternoon the doorbell rang.
I sneaked a look through the window,
hoping it wasn't more reporters.
I was taken aback to see Mike there.
Suddenly I felt very angry.
I hadn't heard from him for days.
Why should I let him in? He had let me down.

He went on ringing the bell.
At last I was forced to answer.
He came into the hall. He pushed me
against the wall and kissed me.
When I could draw breath I slapped
his face – hard.

He looked hurt.
'What was that for?' he asked.
'Aren't you pleased to see me?'
'You must be joking,' I said.
'I don't hear from you at all –
apart from one lousy postcard.
Then you turn up here as if nothing
had happened.'
'Hang on, Liz,' he said.
'You don't understand.
It's all sorted.
Everything's okay.
I've come to tell you you're in the clear.'

I had so many questions to ask.
Mike did his best to answer them.
He and Tim had never believed I was guilty.
'Not for one moment,' he told me.

'Tim had a feeling Jacko was mixed up
with it. But he couldn't prove it.
We let Jacko think it was over.
We hoped he'd give himself away,'
Mike said. 'And he did in time.
You've got Neil to thank for that.
He saw Alan and Jacko talking one day.
They must have thought they were safe.
They knew Neil couldn't hear them.
They didn't realise he could lip read.
Neil saw Alan say to Jacko,
"Your cash is in the usual place."'

Tim tipped off the police.
When they searched Jacko's room they
found a wad of £20 notes and a list.
The list was in Alan's handwriting.
It had the names of horses on it.
Jet's was among them.

There was also a note which said
"Happy Times in the 2 o'clock at York."
The police put a tail on Jacko.

They taped a meeting he had with a lad
from Baxters. And that was that.'
'So Alan was behind it all,' I said.
'Yes,' said Mike.
'He used stable lads to do
his dirty work. Betting's big business.
Alan knew Jet had a good chance of winning
at Hexham. So he put him out of the race.
Jacko phoned you at the course, while
one of Baxters' lads planted the gear on you.'

When Mum and Grandad came back
it was hugs and kisses all round.
Mike drove me back to the stables.
My friends were waiting for me.
We had a party at the pub.
Even Tim came. He was his usual self.
'Don't stay up too late, missie,' he said.
'There's mucking out to be done
in the morning.'
But he patted my arm and I knew
he was glad I was back.

I took Neil to one side to thank him.
He seemed really happy. He had some news too.

With Jacko gone, Mr Mason had picked him
to be an apprentice jockey.
'I'm so pleased for you,' I told him.
'One day you'll be able to ride Jet
and all the other horses I'm going to train.'

Mike must have heard this.
'Oh yes, and what about me?' he asked.
'We'll work together,' I said.
'I'm sure we'll make a winning team.'